SIXTY SECOND SCIENCE

100 SCIENCE
MYTHS EXPLORED

Managing Editor:
Simon Melhuish

Series Editor:
Nikole G. Bamford

Design & Layout:
Linley J. Clode

Compilers and Checkers:
Nick Daws
Tom Melhuish

Published by The Lagoon Group 2010

UK: PO BOX 311, KT2 5QW, UK.
US: 10685-B Hazelhurst Dr. #9988,
Houston, TX 77043, USA.

Printed in China

ISBN: 978-1-907780-07-3

www.thelagoongroup.com

INTRODUCTION

Did you know...

GOLDFISH HAVE A THREE SECOND
MEMORY SPAN.

FINGERPRINTS ARE UNIQUE.

A COIN DROPPED FROM A SKYSCRAPER
WILL KILL A PASSER-BY.

ALL UNTRUE!

Prepare to have your beliefs shattered as
the myths are exploded.

Meet the goldfish who remembers
instructions from three weeks ago.
Discover that being unique means there
could be others with your fingerprints.
Learn that when the penny drops, it will
sting, but not stun.

You will be able to amaze your friends and
enlighten inquisitive kids. Embrace your
inner Einstein.

SIXTY
SECOND
SCIENCE

MYTH!

This commonly-held belief has been proven to be completely false.

Research at the University of Plymouth, England, in 2003 demonstrated that goldfish could learn to remember a daily routine.

The goldfish in the Plymouth study were trained to push a lever in their tank to earn a food reward. When the lever was set to work for only one hour every day, the fish soon learned to operate it at the correct time each day.

Other studies have shown that goldfish have a memory span of at least three months, and can distinguish between different shapes, colors and sounds.

ORIGIN: One (slightly tongue-in-cheek) theory is that this myth arose as a method of making goldfish-owners feel less guilty about keeping their pets in small bowls.

If the fish can't remember anything that happened more than a few seconds ago, so this theory goes, they will never get bored with their tiny homes!

In fact, goldfish are more intelligent than we give them credit for. They can even be taught tricks, such as swimming through a hoop, using the same reward-based training methods used with circus animals.

Goldfish really aren't as stupid as we've been led to believe!

MYTH!

Chewing gum is not a food and is completely indigestible. If swallowed it passes through the digestive system and comes out the other end, basically unchanged, normally within 24 hours.

In a very few cases, children who constantly swallow gum can end up with a blockage in their intestines, but this is rare. Swallowing gum isn't recommended as it has no nutritional value, but if you do accidentally swallow some, it is highly unlikely to cause you any harm.

ORIGIN: This is a common old wives' tale, frequently passed on from parents to children – but there is no truth in it.

We can only speculate that tales about gum remaining in the digestive system for seven years arise from the fact that it quickly becomes an unchanging mass in the mouth that doesn't reduce like food. It's therefore easy to believe it has some special property that allows it to 'stick' inside our body for years on end.

Also, since we know we're not 'supposed' to swallow gum, we imagine sinister-sounding reasons for the prohibition, since the real reason – that it's not a food – is simply far too boring!

It's safe to eat food dropped on the floor if you pick it up within five seconds

MYTH!

This popular myth is often described as 'the five second rule'. There is no scientific support for it, however.

Harmful bacteria on the floor can attach themselves to food dropped on it, even if the food is picked up almost immediately. Other things being equal, the longer the food is left on the floor, the more likely it is to become contaminated. But even five seconds is quite long enough for potentially dangerous bacteria such as salmonella and E. Coli to attach themselves.

ORIGIN: Nobody knows the exact origin of this myth, but it is widely held. One US study found that 56% of men and 70% of women were familiar with the five second rule, and in Russia there is a similar saying, 'promptly picked up is not considered fallen'.

And here are a couple more points to bear in mind. First, a clean-looking floor isn't necessarily clean. A floor that looks dirty is usually worse, but even dry floors that appear spotless may contain bacteria, as some can survive on the floor for a long time. And second, foods with damp surfaces, such as slices of apple, pick up bacteria much more easily than dry foods such as toast.

No doubt about it – however tasty your food, if you've dropped it on the floor, you'd better not eat it!

MYTH!

This is another widely-held myth and it's even appeared in some physics textbooks. It is incorrect, though. Water may drain either way – clockwise or counterclockwise – in either hemisphere. The direction depends on various factors.

ORIGIN: The idea that water drains differently in the Northern and Southern Hemispheres has been popularized by various television programs, including The Simpsons and The X-Files. All this proves is that you shouldn't believe everything you see on TV...

It's true that the Earth's rotation influences some natural phenomena through the so-called Coriolis effect. An example of this is the way weather systems rotate. In the Northern Hemisphere, the direction of movement around a low-pressure area is counterclockwise, while in the Southern Hemisphere it is clockwise. The opposite applies around high-pressure areas.

The Coriolis force is very weak, however. It has only a tiny effect in toilets, basins and bathtubs. The direction water drains out from these depends on other things, most importantly the design of the appliance and the direction the water enters. In addition, most have irregular surfaces and are not perfectly level, which again affects how water drains out. All of these factors overwhelm the slight effect of the Coriolis force.

MYTH!

Contrary to popular belief, lemmings are not suicidal. Indeed it seems unlikely the species would have survived if they regularly did this.

ORIGIN: This story was popularized in a 1958 nature documentary called 'White Wilderness', which appeared to show lemmings hurling themselves off a cliff into the Arctic Ocean. However, it later came to light that the lemmings in the film did not jump voluntarily, but were in fact thrown by a rotating platform installed by the film crew.

Some species of lemmings do perform large-scale migrations though. As they normally inhabit low-lying areas, if a large group find themselves gathered at the top of a cliff, they will instinctively jump over the edge. They are quite good swimmers, however, and usually make it back to dry land.

The reason lemmings perform these mass migrations is still something of a mystery. At one time zoologists thought it was a response to food shortages. However, it has been found that migration patterns do not always coincide with periods when food is in short supply.

In fact, myths and misconceptions about lemmings go back many centuries. In the 1530s, the geographer Zeigler of Strasbourg proposed that the creatures fell out of the sky during stormy weather and then died suddenly when the grass grew in spring. It's safe to say nobody believes that one anymore, though!

MYTH!

It's often claimed celery is a 'negative calorie food' – that you actually use up more calories eating it than it contains. If that were true, it would be the ideal food for anyone looking to lose weight. It's not the case, though.

ORIGIN: This story stems from the fact that celery is a very low-calorie food. An average stalk contains just 10 calories, and does of course require some effort to chew.

Even so, the act of chewing doesn't burn up many calories: about five an hour on average. Even if you took ten minutes to chew your celery, you would barely have burned a single calorie. It's safe to say a calorie deficit will not be created simply by eating celery.

Digesting and metabolizing celery may be another story however. Celery is 95 per cent water, and the rest is mostly cellulose, which is hard for humans to digest. Your body might use up more energy metabolizing celery than it contains, but even if that were true, the calorie deficit would be negligible.

People who experience weight loss eating celery probably do so because it is replacing other high-calorie foods, such as chips or candy, in their diets. This contributes to an overall calorie reduction that induces the body to burn stored fat.

Celery is certainly good for you, and may even help you lose weight, but don't expect to burn off calories just by eating it!

MYTH!

It's widely believed that eating a meal and then going for a swim is highly likely to result in cramps, and death by drowning in the worst-case scenario.

The reality is that you are no more likely to suffer cramps following food than from having an empty stomach. In addition, cramps, while undoubtedly painful, can be easily relieved, and are very unlikely to be fatal.

ORIGIN: Parents often tell their children to wait 30 minutes or an hour after having a meal before they swim. This advice that has been handed down over generations doesn't hold water though.

The myth is based on the mistaken idea that the stomach will take away some of the oxygen needed by our muscles during swimming. In reality, however, most people have more than enough oxygen to supply both the stomach and their skeletal muscles. It is therefore very unlikely that swimming soon after a meal will leave someone in so much distress that they drown.

Competitive swimmers, though, generally shouldn't eat a large meal before an event because there's a risk this could hinder their performance.

While eating before swimming is fine, drinking is not advisable. A study published in the journal Pediatrics found that a quarter of teenagers who drowned were intoxicated. A similar study on adults found that 41 per cent of drowning deaths involved alcohol.

So eating a light meal before swimming is fine, but don't wash it down with a few beers!

MYTH!

This is one of those 'conspiracy' tales that keeps resurfacing no matter how many times it is denied.

The story goes that the brace position was actually designed by the airline industry to kill people rather than protect them during a crash, to save money by paying off wrongful death suits rather than more costly disability compensations.

Few people seriously believe airlines would treat passengers with such disdain and all the evidence shows that the brace position does actually improve your chances of surviving a crash.

ORIGIN: There is one grain of truth in this story, in that the average amount paid by airlines in wrongful death suits is actually lower than the amount paid for disability compensation. So, viewed purely from an accountancy perspective, killing passengers is cheaper for airlines than seriously injuring them. Still, there is no evidence they have ever tried to capitalize on this.

Many people believe that if they're in a plane crash, their time is up. In fact, the truth is surprisingly different. In the US alone, between 1983 and 2000, there were 568 plane crashes. Out of a total of 53,487 people on board, 51,207 survived. Advances in science and technology now mean that over 90 per cent of plane crashes have survivors. Adopting the brace position improves your chances of being among them, because it stops you jerking forward and striking the seat in front of you.

Happy flying!

MYTH!

Diamonds are the hardest natural materials known. They can certainly scratch glass, but so can plenty of other substances.

There are various methods for measuring hardness. One is to use a scratch test such as Moh's Scale. This lists diamonds at 10 (the maximum), corundum (ruby and sapphire) at 9, topaz at 8, quartz at 7, feldspar at 6, and so on. Glass varies a bit according to its composition, but it is generally around 5.5.

At each step the next material up the scale is capable of scratching its lower neighbor. It's easy to see from this that there are many materials that will scratch or cut glass, therefore.

ORIGIN: It seems to have become an urban myth that only a diamond can cut glass, but obviously fake diamonds can mark glass too.

One reason this myth is still widely believed is due to dishonest traders. Some such individuals, offering imitation diamonds, attempt to mislead potential buyers with such claims as 'It Even Cuts Glass!' This is no proof they are real diamonds, however.

Because of their extreme hardness, the only natural object that can scratch a diamond is another diamond. This is one of the many features that make them so desirable for jewelry, of course. But if anyone tries to convince you a diamond is genuine because it can score glass, it is probably time for a 'sharp' exit!

10   If you are stung by a jellyfish someone should urinate on the sting

MYTH!

This is an old wives' tale. Doing it could actually make matters worse.

ORIGIN: If you have someone urinate on the sting, it may appear to be working at first. This is because the acid in the urine may neutralize the stinging sensation for a short period.

This relief is temporary at best. Furthermore, because of toxins in the urine, the sting could become infected. If you are stung by a jellyfish, the recommended advice is to check for and remove any loose tentacles that may still be on your skin, then immerse the affected area in warm water.

11   Daddy-longlegs are more venomous than spiders

MYTH!

The story goes that daddy-longlegs are the most venomous animals on earth – but luckily, because of their tiny mouths, they can't bite humans. This is incorrect though. When people make this claim, they are usually referring to the daddy-longlegs spider, but there is no evidence these small creatures are especially venomous.

ORIGIN: This myth may stem from the fact that daddy-longlegs spiders prey on deadly species such as redbacks. It was once thought that if they could kill another spider capable of delivering fatal bites to humans, they must be even more venomous. In reality, however, the daddy-longlegs spider is merely quicker than the redback.

MYTH!

Not even close. Dinosaurs became extinct approximately 65 million years ago. Our first primitive ape ancestors are thought to have emerged 23 million years ago, while homo sapiens (with modern human features) first appeared only around 130,000 years ago.

Nobody knows for sure why the dinosaurs became extinct, but they disappeared in quite a short space of time. The most popular theory is that this occurred as the result of a dramatic climate change caused by an asteroid hitting the Earth, although this is a moot point.

However, there is evidence that some dinosaurs evolved into modern-day birds. So if you really stretch a point, you could say that modern human beings lived at the same time as these dinosaur relatives – but, of course, this is not what most people mean by dinosaurs.

ORIGIN: Through fossils, we have a very good idea of what the dinosaurs looked like, and most of us have seen pictures and models in books and museums. These inevitably include a degree of artistic license, as nobody can know for sure what dinosaurs looked like externally. But these images have become so familiar, it's easy to imagine that dinosaurs lived at the same time as us.

And, of course, the long-running cartoon series The Flintstones, which showed 'Stone Age' human beings co-existing with dinosaurs, has contributed to this impression. Sadly, though, a human family could never have kept a dinosaur as a pet!

MYTH!

It is often said that you can outwit a crocodile by running in a zigzag manner away from it. This isn't true, though.

Humans can outrun crocodiles on land, and a straight line is the fastest way of putting distance between yourself and the crocodile. In fact, most crocodile attack victims never see the crocodile coming – the animals rely on surprise, not speed.

ORIGIN: One of the biggest myths about crocodiles is that they can run at high speed. Speeds of over 40 mph/64 kph are regularly quoted by some books, television documentaries and over-enthusiastic tour guides.

The reality is that crocodiles aren't built for speed. Their typical hunting strategy is one of surprise, lunging at prey and capturing it in a single quick movement. Crocodiles have relatively low stamina and their physiology does not allow sustained exercise. When a crocodile runs, it is nearly always away from a potential threat and into the water. Most crocodiles can achieve speeds of around 8 mph/13 kph for short periods, which is somewhat slower than a fit human can run.

It follows that, if you're reasonably fit, you can definitely outrun a crocodile. There's no need to zigzag to try and confuse him!

MYTH!

Despite what your parents may have told you, there is no substance that will reveal the presence of urine in a public swimming pool.

Although in theory such a substance might be developed, it would be difficult to create one that did not also respond to other organic substances (sweat, for example) often found in pool water.

In addition, it is quite likely that the presence of any such compound would have the opposite effect to that intended. Kids being kids, if word got around that peeing in a certain pool turned it red, many would be queuing up to try this out for themselves. And, of course, it would be easy enough to pin the blame on another swimmer who happened to be passing by.

ORIGIN: Nobody knows the origins of this myth, but it is widely believed across the world, including the United States, Canada and Spain.

The story is probably perpetuated by teachers, parents and swimming pool managers, who wish to discourage this particular form of anti-social – and unhygienic – behavior.

There is no such substance, however, and it is highly unlikely there ever will be!

MYTH!

This is a common claim (and a popular theme for science fair projects). It's almost certainly untrue, however.

Dogs use their mouths for a wide range of things humans don't, including many that have high potential for picking up bacteria. These include washing themselves, chewing and eating items from the trash, and drinking muddy water. And, unlike human beings, dogs also use their mouths as toilet paper.

It's highly unlikely that any dog's mouth would be cleaner than a human's, therefore.

ORIGIN: One reason for this notion was the belief, once widely accepted, that dog bites were less likely to become infected than human bites. Recent studies have cast doubt on this, however. Apart from bites on the hand (where other considerations apply), the rate of infection for both human and dog bites is about 10 per cent.

A further factor is that scientists have found that humans are more at risk of acquiring an illness if they come into mouth-to-mouth contact with another human, and the same goes for dogs whose mouths come into contact with those of other dogs. The reason is that there are few infections that can be transmitted between the two species, so a human being is much more likely to get ill from contact with another human.

So, if you're a dog owner, you can take comfort in knowing that a kiss from your dog may be unpleasant, but it is unlikely to cause you any health problems!

16 You can't teach an old dog new tricks

MYTH!

This is not the case. The presenters of the Discovery Channel TV show MythBusters demonstrated this in 2007, when they taught two seven-year-old dogs (the human equivalent of 50) to heel, sit, lie down, stay and shake hands on command. The training took just four days, and the dogs had never learned any similar skills before.

ORIGIN: This myth may have its roots way back in 1523, when an English author named Fitzherbert wrote in his treatise on animal husbandry that 'the dogge must lerne when he is a whelpe, or els it wyl not be; for it is harde to make an old dogge to stoupe.' This is, of course, the old English equivalent of 'You can't teach an old dog new tricks.'

Since then this has become a well-known proverb, and it is regularly applied to human beings as well. But it's just as false for us. Some abilities such as languages and sports are most easily learned in childhood and adolescence, but we remain able to acquire new skills deep into old age.

'You can't teach an old dog new tricks' is definitely NOT an acceptable excuse for not trying to learn something new!

MYTH!

This is one of those urban legends that has been repeated so many times many people assume it must be true. It's not, though.

In fact, the Inuit or Eskimo people have only two basic words for snow: 'qanniq' ('qanik' in some dialects), which is used like the English verb 'to snow', and 'aput', which means snow as a substance.

ORIGIN: This myth probably arose from a misunderstanding of how the Inuit language works. Very long words can be formed in the language by adding more and more descriptive prefixes and suffixes to words. These modify the meaning of the original word, in much the same way that in English we add adjectives or descriptive phrases to describe things more precisely (e.g. 'fresh snow', 'falling snow', 'snow on the ground', and so on).

Where English would use two or three words for this purpose, the Inuits simply add prefixes and suffixes to the base word.

The myth probably lives on because people like to quote it as an example of the power of language to affect our view of the world. The presumption is that the Inuits somehow 'see' snow differently (and perhaps more accurately) because of all the different words they have to describe it. It's a nice idea – and probably valid in other contexts – but, in the case of the Inuit language, the basic concept is simply wrong.

MYTH!

If you're going out in the cold it's likely you've been told to put on a hat, since 'most of your body heat is lost through your head.'

It's a widely-held belief, but there is no truth in it. In fact, you lose no more and no less heat through your head than any other part of your body.

ORIGIN: In a 2008 article in the British Medical Journal, Indiana University scientists Rachel Vreeman and Aaron Carroll traced this myth back to a US army survival manual from 1970. This strongly recommended covering the head when it was cold, since (it stated) 40 to 45 per cent of body heat was lost from the head.

This assertion was probably based on a flawed interpretation of research by the US military in the 1950s. In these studies, volunteers were dressed in Arctic survival suits and exposed to bitterly cold conditions. Because it was the only part of their bodies left uncovered, most of their body heat was lost through their heads. However, this does not prove that in normal conditions most heat would be lost this way.

In fact, covering one part of the body has as much effect as any other. According to Vreeman and Carroll, if the experiment had been performed with people wearing only swimming trunks, they would have lost no more than 10 per cent of their body heat through their head.

MYTH!

This is another widely-held belief with no factual basis. A calorie is a calorie whenever you eat it.

This was confirmed in a 2003 study by scientists at Oregon Health and Science University. They examined the eating habits of rhesus monkeys, using them to help understand human obesity.

The scientists found that the monkeys who ate most of their food at night were at no greater risk of gaining weight than those who chose to eat earlier in the day. Such evidence supports the claims of many health professionals that it is the amount of calories you eat, not the time of day you eat them, that determines the amount of weight you gain.

ORIGIN: There is one grain of truth in this statement, which is that people who eat late at night often do so not because they are truly hungry, but out of habit or because they are bored. They typically eat less healthily, choosing 'comfort foods' such as chips, cookies, chocolate, pizza, and so on.

The calories from such foods add up quickly, and can easily increase our daily intake well above the level required to meet our energy needs. The excess calories are then deposited as fat.

If you know you're guilty of this yourself, avoiding eating after dinner may help prevent you putting on weight. But if you miss a healthy dinner at 6 o'clock, there's no reason not to eat it at 9 o'clock!

20 You taste sweet, salt, sour and bitter on different parts of the tongue

MYTH!

This theory was once generally accepted and taught in schools. It proposed that each part of the tongue can detect just one of the four basic tastes, as set out below.

1. The back of the tongue: bitter.

2. The sides of the tongue near the back: sour.

3. The sides of the tongue near the front: salty.

4. The tip of the tongue: sweet.

This idea has long been disproved. In fact, every part of the tongue can sense every basic taste. The latest research also indicates that there may be more than four basic tastes. The existence of a fifth taste, savoriness (also known as 'umami' in Japanese), is now widely accepted, and some authorities believe there may be others as well.

ORIGIN: This theory had its origins in the 'tongue maps' or 'taste maps' that at one time appeared regularly in academic textbooks.

These in turn derived from a 1942 paper written by Harvard psychologist Edwin G. Boring, which was a translation of a German paper written in 1901 by D.P. Hanig. The unclear representation of data in Boring's paper was taken by some readers to imply that each part of the tongue detects just one basic taste, though the original research by Hanig didn't support this. So the myth began, and even though it was discredited by the 1970s, it is still widely believed even today.

MYTH!

The number of legs on a centipede can actually vary from 30 to 382, according to the species. Centipedes have one pair of legs on each body segment. Since most centipedes have fewer than 50 segments, most have fewer than 100 legs.

ORIGIN: The name centipede means 'one hundred legs', so it's not difficult to see where this myth began.

Interestingly enough, though, while centipede species have been found with more than 100 legs as well as less than 100, not a single one has ever been found with exactly 100. The closest was a species, discovered in 1999, which has 96!

MYTH!

According to this urban legend, the sugar dissolves in the gasoline and gets into the engine. Here the heat melts it into a thick sludge that gets into every nook and cranny, and hardens to a rock-like consistency when it cools. This doesn't happen, though, the main reason being that sugar doesn't dissolve in gasoline. If it gets into the fuel system, it's trapped by the fuel filter and doesn't enter the engine itself. It may clog the filter, but it's unlikely to cause any serious damage.

ORIGIN: This myth's popularity is probably due to the potential it appears to offer for low-cost revenge. Perhaps fortunately, therefore, it just doesn't work!

MYTH!

The story goes that if you use a cellphone while flying, the signal can interfere with the plane's navigation systems, possibly leading to a crash.

While there is a very small theoretical possibility of this happening, there is no proof it has ever occurred in practice. Aircraft navigation systems are designed to continue working even in the middle of an electrical storm, so it is very unlikely that the low-energy signals from a cellphone could interfere with them.

ORIGIN: Some crews have reported interference with their instruments caused by passengers using cellphones. This has never been proved, however. Even when aircraft manufacturer Boeing bought some of the suspect devices from passengers, they were unable to reproduce the effects reported by the crew.

ABC News 20/20 aired a report in December 2007 trying to get to the bottom of the cellphone ban. They concluded that the main reason it existed was that the regulatory authorities were unwilling to spend the money to perform conclusive safety tests. They have left this up to the airlines, who do not see any benefit to themselves in paying for such tests.

In practice, a growing number of airlines do now allow cellphone use during flights. And new technologies such as picocells have been devised to reduce the very small theoretical risk even further.

So don't expect your flight to be a peaceful, phone-free zone for very much longer!

MYTH!

This is one of those 'facts' many of us take as gospel. And yet it is almost certainly untrue.

Logically, there is no way we could ever be sure of this. Unless you compare the fingerprints of everyone on the planet, it's impossible to be certain two or more aren't identical. There is also more concrete evidence that fingerprints may not be as unique as we've been led to believe.

ORIGIN: The claim that no fingerprint has ever occurred twice was first made over a hundred years ago – and by relentless repetition and lack of contradiction, it was soon widely accepted as fact.

The claim lent the technique of forensic fingerprint analysis an aura of infallibility, and it came to be regarded as a perfect system of identification. As a result, examiners' testimony at criminal trials came to be almost unassailable.

Until recently, that is. In 1998, in Delaware County, Pa., Richard Jackson was sentenced to life in prison for murder, based largely on a fingerprint match to which three experts had testified. The defense argued, unsuccessfully, that it was a bad match. But after Jackson spent more than two years in prison, the prosecution conceded the error, and he was freed.

As this and several other recent cases indicate, the important question isn't really whether fingerprints are unique – it's whether they are ever similar enough to fool a fingerprint examiner. And the answer to that is a clear yes.

25 Some tooth fillings can pick up radio broadcasts

MYTH!

The story that some people are able to pick up radio broadcasts through their fillings has been around for many years. There is still no authenticated proof that it has ever occurred, however.

ORIGIN: She may not have been the first to make the claim, but this story got a considerable boost when, in a 1975 TV interview, comedienne Lucille Ball revealed it had happened to her.

According to Lucy, in 1942 – when the US had just entered the war – she had recently had several temporary fillings fitted. One evening, when driving home from the MGM studios, she started hearing music in her mouth. A week later her mouth started jumping again, and this time it was Morse code. Lucy said she alerted the authorities, and when they investigated they discovered an underground Japanese radio station. As a result, several Japanese spies were arrested.

Although this story sounds alluring, it is actually pretty implausible, not least because it is doubtful whether 'Japanese spies' would have been using Morse code. And there was surprisingly little publicity about the incident at the time.

The US TV show MythBusters investigated this in 2003. They tried to reproduce the effect using gold and amalgam fillings, but were unsuccessful. They suggested that Lucy's supposed Morse code pick-up might actually have been an electrical reaction between the fillings and her saliva. Still, none of this has stopped many people believing the story is true!

MYTH!

There are many variations on this story, but basically they all concern a woman who wants to look her best for a big day. She treats herself to too many tanning sessions, and cooks herself from the inside out.

In fact, this is a total myth. Tanning booths do not use microwave radiation (which cooks evenly inside and out). Tanning booths work on ultraviolet radiation, which penetrates the body from the outside in, meaning that all one would get is a bad case of sunburn.

ORIGIN: Nobody knows exactly where this story originated, but in 1987 it apparently erupted out of thin air. Even advice columnist Abigail van Buren was drawn into the search for 'the broiled girl'. But despite the huge interest the story generated, the young woman in question was never found.

It now seems likely that the story was rooted in a growing distrust of modern technology and confusion with microwave cookers. Even in these more health-conscious times, the tale still continues to do the rounds.

Of course, we now know that overuse of tanning booths does present some serious health risks, particularly with regard to skin cancer. For that reason, they need to be used with caution, and following the advice of a qualified professional. But nobody has ever cooked their insides in a tanning booth!

MYTH!

This is another of those 'facts' that appears regularly in trivia lists, and yet it is untrue.

Anyone who believes this should ask themselves why a duck's quack wouldn't echo. What could be so special about the sound a duck makes that exempts it from the physical laws that apply to every other sound, including a dog's bark, a cat's meow or a lamb's bleat? The answer is nothing.

ORIGIN: Nobody is sure where this myth originated, but it was investigated recently by acoustic engineers at the University of Salford in England. They placed a duck called Daisy in a reverberation chamber and recorded the sound of her quacking. Their tests clearly showed that echoes were produced.

The Salford scientists suggested three reasons for the persistence of this myth...

1. The quack does echo, but it is often too quiet to hear.

2. Ducks don't usually quack near reflecting surfaces. You need a large reflecting surface, such as a mountain or tall building, for the sound to reflect off.

3. Ducks quack repeatedly and the sound fades in and out. As a listener, it can be hard to tell whether you're hearing the quack itself or an echo.

But ducks' calls definitely produce echoes. Anyone who tells you otherwise is simply quackers!

MYTH!

We've all heard the story which generally concerns a woman with breast implants going on a plane journey. The reduced air pressure in the cabin causes her implants to expand massively and (in some versions) explode.

This is another of those stories with no truth to it. Breast implants do not get bigger in the lower pressure of an airplane cabin, let alone explode.

ORIGIN: This story probably stems from a confusion with balloons, which because they are filled with gas (usually hot air or helium) do indeed expand when the air pressure around them is reduced. Breast implants do not contain gas, however. They contain either a silicone-based gel or a saline water solution. These substances do not expand like gases in the slightly reduced cabin pressure.

This story has formed the basis of several April Fool's Day pranks, including one in 2006 in the British tabloid newspaper The Sun. Their story claimed that women with breast implants were to be banned from Sir Richard Branson's planned Virgin Galactic service, due to fears their implants might explode as the shuttle zoomed to 400,000 feet above the Earth. Quite a few people were fooled by the story, which also claimed passengers would have to wear diapers because there were no toilets on board!

MYTH!

Just as a coin dropped from the top of a tall building wouldn't kill you, the same applies to a bullet falling from the sky. Atmospheric resistance would slow the falling bullet to a speed that would be painful but almost certainly not fatal.

There's one proviso, however. The bullet would have to be dropped from a stationary point or fired vertically upward before descending. If the bullet is fired at an angle, it could still be lethal on its descent.

ORIGIN: To understand the above, a bit of science is required.

If you fire a bullet straight in the air, it travels upward till all the energy from the powder is expended. At this point it is pulled back to earth by gravity, but slowed by air resistance.

Bullets are small and aerodynamic, but when falling from stationary they still only achieve a maximum speed of around 100 miles/160 km per hour. The minimum speed for a bullet to penetrate flesh is around 200 miles/320 km per hour. So a falling bullet would barely break your skin, let alone kill you.

If the bullet isn't fired straight, it's a different story. In this case, the bullet will travel in an arc. Gravity will pull it back to earth, but not before the momentum from the initial blast has been exhausted. This means the bullet could still be moving fast enough to be lethal.

MYTH!

The implication here is that heavy boots somehow keep astronauts attached to the surface of their craft, but this is not the case. Although every object possesses some gravitational attraction, with a spacecraft this is tiny. It would certainly not be enough to keep an astronaut attached, however heavy the boots!

ORIGIN: People who believe this are getting confused with the situation on Earth, where the force of gravity is much stronger. If you are wearing heavy boots on Earth, you are of course unlikely to be able to jump very high!

In fact, when astronauts go on spacewalks, they use safety tethers to stay close to their craft. One end of the tether is hooked to the astronaut and the other end to the craft.

Another way astronauts stay safe on spacewalks is by wearing a SAFER, which stands for 'Simplified Aid for EVA Rescue'. SAFER is worn like a backpack and uses small jet thrusters to let an astronaut move around in space. If an astronaut became untethered and floated away, SAFER would help him or her fly back to the spacecraft. Astronauts control SAFER with a small joystick, just like a video game.

In theory it might be possible for astronauts to use magnetic boots to stay attached to their craft on spacewalks, but in practice this is not done because of the potential for magnetic interference with navigation and communication systems.

MYTH!

ORIGIN: This amazing 'fact' is regularly trotted out at quizzes, and yet it's totally false. Hair and fingernails do NOT carry on growing after death – perhaps our forebears were confused because it is actually an optical illusion, caused by the flesh drying out after death and retracting. Hair also takes hundreds of years to decompose so when bodies have been disinterred from centuries gone by, the skeletons would still have hair.

When our flesh dries out it shrinks. It therefore pulls away from the hair and nails, making them look longer. So, for example, the nail on our big toe remains the same size, but because the flesh around it pulls back, the effect is to make it look as if it has grown. Likewise, the beard on a man's face looks as if it is growing as the skin retracts. To combat this effect, funeral homes slather moisturizing cream over the faces of their clients, particularly those of men with beards.

As a matter of interest, among the living, fingernails typically grow at about a tenth of a ml a day, with toenails growing about a half to a third slower. After we pop our clogs, however, all growth of hair and nails almost immediately stops.

MYTH!

There is no credible evidence this has ever happened, either now or in the past. And it's very unlikely alligators would live long in the sewers anyway. For one thing it's too cold, and for another they would not survive the high levels of bacteria and other toxins.

ORIGIN: The story goes that baby alligators brought back from Florida as pets were dumped in the sewers when they got too big, and unexpectedly thrived.

It's a plausible-sounding story, but there are no verified sightings to support it. Most reported incidents have turned out to be animals that escaped from zoos, and in some cases not alligators at all but lizards.

MYTH!

'Sweat like a pig' is an expression meaning to sweat heavily, as in 'I was so nervous, I was sweating like a pig.' This is based on a myth, however. Pigs actually have very few sweat glands. This means they can't sweat to lose heat, which is why on hot days they wallow in the mud or puddles to keep cool.

ORIGIN: Nobody is sure where this expression originated. One theory is that pigs smell, and people simply assumed that sweat was the cause. Another theory is that it may have evolved from an older (17th century) expression, 'bleed like a stuck pig'. But the truth is you really can't sweat like a pig!

MYTH!

Many of us, when looking at camels in the zoo, still believe their humps are filled with water. That's not the case, though. A camel's hump, or humps – some species have two – is actually a food reserve.

ORIGIN: It's common knowledge that camels can survive for many days in the hot desert without access to water. So many of us simply assume they carry a supply of water around in their hump.

This is easily disproved by cutting into it. Such an action would reveal that the hump is mostly fat, which is absorbed as nutrition when food is scarce.

So how do camels survive so long without water? The answer is that when camels find water, they drink a lot of it. A camel can consume 80–100 liters/17.5–22 gallons of water in just ten minutes. The camel's gut releases this water slowly over time, so as not to overload the animal's metabolism. Camels also have an exceptional ability to minimize their water losses. They don't sweat, for example, and produce very little urine.

Although it's a myth that their humps are filled with water, this does not alter the fact that camels are amazing animals, wonderfully adapted to living in harsh, desert conditions.

MYTH!

With gas prices going through the roof, there is no doubt that the prospect of running cars on water is a highly attractive one. Unfortunately, it is unlikely ever to happen.

The basic problem is that water is a low-energy compound. It is abundant largely because it has very stable chemical bonds that resist most reactions. Water won't even burn in pure oxygen. For it to take part in a reaction that releases energy, high-energy compounds must be added to it. For example, it is possible to produce the combustible fuel acetylene by adding calcium carbide to water. However, the calcium carbide requires a lot of energy to make in the first place. The calcium carbide is really the fuel, therefore, not the water it reacts with.

ORIGIN: Water-fueled cars have been the subject of numerous international patents, newspaper and science magazine articles, local TV news coverage, and stories on the internet. The claims made for all of these devices remain unproven, and some have even turned out to be tied to investment frauds.

Stories of water-fueled cars continue to circulate largely because the idea is so appealing – and, of course, if anyone really was able to construct such a vehicle, they (and anybody investing in them) would be sitting on a fortune. The laws of physics, however, strongly suggest that water-fueled cars are destined to remain forever in the realms of science fiction.

MYTH!

Like the story that blondes will be extinct within two hundred years, this is a myth, albeit one that has been widely circulated.

ORIGIN: This story is based on one true fact, which is that in many parts of the world the proportion of people with blue eyes is declining. The reasons for this have to do with immigration patterns, intermarriage, and genetics.

A hundred years ago, roughly half the American population had blue eyes. By around 1950, the ratio had dipped to about one in three. Nowadays, only about one in every six Americans has blue eyes.

One major reason for this is changing marriage patterns. In the past most people married somebody within their own ethnic group, but that is far less true now. Blue eyes are a recessive trait, which means that unless both parents pass on the gene for blue eyes to their offspring, they will have brown or green eyes instead. The blue-eye gene is less common in some ethnic groups, so the chances of the children of such marriages having blue eyes are significantly less.

Even though blue eyes are becoming less common, this doesn't mean they will disappear any time soon. Because blue eyes are a recessive trait, many people without them still carry the gene and can pass it on to their children. Blue eyes will therefore almost certainly be with us for many centuries to come!

MYTH!

It would be nice if, like Doctor Who, we could regenerate at regular intervals, but it's not the case. If it were, presumably we would live forever.

ORIGIN: This is another of those stories that has its origins in fact. It is indeed the case that some cells in the human body die and are replaced a number of times during our lifetime (the cells in our bones take longest, living for up to 10 years).

It is misleading to say that your whole body 'renews' itself. Muscles can regenerate but will only do so if seriously injured. The cells in the cerebral and visual cortex haven't been proved to renew. Also the dermis doesn't behave in the same way as the constantly renewing epidermis since if it did then scars or tattoos would disappear over time. They may fade or disperse slightly but they remain.

However most cells in your body do have a limited lifespan and are replaced when they die. This process of replacing cells, while remarkable in many ways, is not perfect. The replaced tissue will contain small errors, which is the reason that we age. Increasing the rate of tissue damage (the rate at which cells need to be replaced) by such things as smoking, drinking, exposure to environmental pollution, and so on, all accelerate this process.

Unless you're a Time Lord and immune to such things, therefore, it's best to give your body all the help you can, so that it doesn't have to replace itself too often!

MYTH!

The radiation emitted by radioactive substances consists of very energetic X-rays (called gamma rays) and small particles such as electrons and neutrons that fly out carrying a lot of energy.

For the most part, human beings cannot sense these rays directly. That is one reason radiation is so dangerous to us – you can easily get a lethal dose without realizing that anything is wrong.

One way radioactive things can appear to glow is when they are placed in something transparent like water. Some of the particles that fly out, like electrons, can be going so fast that they go faster than light does in that medium (light travels slower in water than it does in air). This causes them to emit a pale blue light, called Cerenkov radiation. This is the blue glow people sometimes associate with nuclear reactors.

ORIGIN: The 'glowing green' story has its origins in the old 'radium watch dials'. These used a little bit of radioactive material mixed with a phosphor as a cheap way of providing light without the need for a battery. When the radiation struck the phosphors on the dial, it made the numbers glow green. Such watches are no longer produced, as we now realize that wearing even a weak source of radiation on your wrist is undesirable.

So radioactive substances don't glow green – but when radiation strikes some other clear substances, it might give off a faint colored light!

MYTH!

Not all white cats are deaf, although deafness is more common among these animals.

ORIGIN: This myth has its origins in fact. Among cats in general, those that are pure white with blue eyes are very likely to be deaf. This is believed to be because the gene that causes the fur to be white also affects the development of the cat's inner ear, causing deafness, but this is not invariably the case. For example, the Turkish Van Kedisi is a pure white cat with blue eyes, but it usually has normal hearing.

White cats with green or gold eyes are less likely than those with blue eyes to be deaf. Deafness in these cases is an inherited condition, and there is no cure for it.

Even cats that are deaf usually manage to lead happy, contented lives. They may be more at risk than their hearing counterparts as they will be less aware of oncoming danger, so many owners prefer to keep them in the house, away from traffic, dogs, and so on. These cats can still can feel vibrations in the ground, and – like deaf humans – often compensate for their lack of hearing by developing their other senses. Having nine lives probably comes in handy as well!

MYTH!

This is one of those urban legends that has been repeated so many times many people assume it must be true. The folklore from the countryside has been handed down through generations but isn't necessarily rooted in scientific fact.

Unfortunately, cows lying down before rain doesn't seem to be the most accurate weather predictor. Cows lying down in a field more often means they're chewing their cud, rather than preparing for rainfall. They also just lie down to rest or nurture their calves.

In a country where the probability is that it rains a lot, some cows will always be lying down just before it rains. Similarly, some will be standing.

ORIGIN: There is some proven truth in old weather folklore but this is an unproven belief. Cows aren't dumb animals. They do tend to bunch together when the weather is bad, to protect each other. They also put their rear ends to the wind as a form of protection. If there is cover available when it's raining, like barns or trees, they will head for shelter. All these are great indicators of their common sense but it doesn't prove they are great weather predictors.

MYTH!

We've all heard the expression 'running around like a headless chicken'. In reality, this just doesn't happen, though.

Like all mammals, movement in chickens is controlled by the brain, which is contained in the animal's head. If this is chopped off, controlled movement such as running or walking is impossible.

There may still be some movement in the chicken's body caused by random nerve impulses, but this doesn't last long. One study of broiler hens at the University of Georgia found that such activity in most headless chickens lasted no longer than 60 seconds, and 90 seconds in the most extreme case.

ORIGIN: This myth may have its roots in a true story. Back in 1945, a chicken named Mike in Fruita, Colorado, lived for 18 months after having his head chopped off. During this time he lived a normal life, growing from 2½ to nearly 8 pounds, and became a national celebrity.

It turned out that there was a logical explanation. Mike the Headless Chicken was not beheaded completely. Scientists who came to investigate found that the farmer had chopped the chicken's head high, aiming to leave a generous neck bone, and left most of his brain stem intact. Since most of a chicken's reflex actions are controlled by the brain stem, Mike was able to remain quite healthy.

So Miracle Mike, as he was also known, wasn't quite the miracle he first appeared!

MYTH!

There have been persistent rumors linking cellphone use with cancer. Extensive ongoing research, however, has failed to prove any definite link yet but scientists are still unsure.

ORIGIN: Cellphones are low-powered radio devices that transmit and receive microwave radiation. When you use a cellphone, your body absorbs a certain amount of this radiation. This has therefore led to concerns that it might increase the risk of cancer, and specifically brain tumors.

Several research studies carried out in Europe and the US have looked at large numbers of people using cellphones. Most have found no link between brain tumors and phone use. One of the largest studies was carried out in Denmark and followed over 400,000 people, some for as long as 21 years. In December 2006, the Danish researchers published a paper that looked particularly at people who had been using a cellphone for more than 10 years. They found no increased risk of brain tumors in this group.

It's also worth remembering that most of the research carried out has looked at older analog phones. The majority of cellphones sold nowadays are digital. These give out less radiation than analog phones, and so any potential risk is reduced.

Even so, because no-one can be absolutely sure about the possible dangers, experts generally recommend that cellphones are only used for short calls and preferably with a hands-free kit.

MYTH!

Although this claim is still made regularly, it's been proved false. Sharks definitely do get cancer, and both benign and malignant tumors have been discovered among them.

ORIGIN: Bottles of shark cartilage pills can be bought in health food stores and over the internet allegedly possessing cancer fighting powers. Their cartilage is sold based on the commonly held belief that sharks do not get cancer. Sharks have been around for over 400 million years and they certainly have higher resistance to disease. The presence of cancerous tumors in sharks is definitely lower than in humans but sharks are not cancer-free. For many years the lack of study into shark anatomy and disease allowed this myth to continue.

The first shark tumor was recorded in 1908. In April 2000, scientists demonstrated 40 benign and cancerous tumors known to be found in sharks. It was discovered that as in humans, tumors grow in sharks as a response to environmental toxins and pollutants. In fact, sharks are extra-sensitive to pollutants, which may actually make them more susceptible to tumors.

Unfortunately this myth has led to the destruction of many shark species. Despite over 100 years of recorded cases of shark tumors plus scientific evidence that shark cartilage is not a cure for cancer, sharks continue to be killed for the alternative health industry. Perhaps now that sharks have been proven to get poorly too, people might be a little more sympathetic to them.

MYTH!

Leprosy (also known as Hansen's disease) doesn't cause any body parts to fall off. The disease affects the nerves in the hands and feet, eventually causing them to lose all sensation. In one form of the disease lumps and patches can appear all over the body, causing deformities but they take months and years to develop.

Thankfully, nowadays, leprosy is fully curable with antibiotics. Doctors are even trying to develop a vaccine for it which can be administered in countries where the disease still prevails, like India and Brazil.

ORIGIN: While leprosy doesn't cause limbs to drop off in itself, the loss of sensation in the arms and legs makes it more likely sufferers will lose fingers, toes or limbs through infection or accident.

In addition, numb feet are more susceptible to ulcers. If not treated and cared for properly, this can result in the sufferer needing to have a foot or part of a leg amputated.

Before the advent of successful treatments, lepers were segregated from society, although leprosy is not highly contagious. Even the lepers referred to in biblical texts were deemed 'unclean' and ordered to 'live alone'. The strange thing about these lepers is that, due to an error in translation, the Biblical 'leprosy' is actually a blanket term used for skin complaints like eczema or psoriasis. And having either of these certainly doesn't make your limbs drop off.

MYTH!

Stainless steel is an iron alloy containing at least 10.5 per cent chromium. Stainless steel does not stain, corrode, or rust as easily as ordinary steel, but it is definitely not stain-proof.

ORIGIN: 'Stainless steel' was originally a marketing term used to describe cutlery made with this substance. It was adopted as a general name for these steels, and now covers a wide range of steel types and grades where resistance to corrosion is important.

A more accurate term than stainless, however, would be stain-resistant. Stainless steel items should never be soaked for long periods or put in high-concentration bleach solutions or saltwater, as they may well become corroded. A stainless steel knife placed in contact with a metal pan can pick up a stain due to the chemical reaction of the two metal items in combination with hot water and dishwasher detergent.

Stainless steel's resistance to corrosion and staining, relatively low cost and attractive luster make it well-suited to a host of commercial applications. These include cutlery, kitchen equipment, jewelry, food storage tanks, firearms, garden tools, and decorative features on buildings and automobiles. Another benefit of stainless steel in these environmentally conscious times is that it is 100 per cent recyclable. All in all, while it may not be strictly stainless, it's still a very useful substance!

MYTH!

Neither can you see the stars during the day from the bottom of a mineshaft or the similar places some people claim.

The reason you can't see the stars here is the same as on the surface. During the day, light from the Sun is scattered across the sky by dust in the atmosphere. If you are at the bottom of a well, all you will see is the same blue sky you would see at the top. The daytime sky is much brighter than the light from most stars, and simply drowns it out.

At night it's a different story, of course. At this time there is no dispersed sunlight to block your view, so you can see right through the atmosphere into space.

ORIGIN: This mistaken notion was first mentioned by Aristotle and other ancient sources. It was believed by many people in the 19th century, and even by some astronomers. But every astronomer who tried this personally has come away convinced it was impossible.

Experiments to try to see Vega and Pollux through tall chimneys were performed by J. A. Hynek and A. N. Winsor. They were unable to detect these stars under near-perfect conditions, even with binoculars. The daytime sky is simply too bright to allow us to see the stars. Standing at the bottom of a well makes absolutely no difference to this.

MYTH!

This is simply untrue. The effect of gravity diminishes with distance, but it never truly goes away.

Indeed, the universe would be a very different place if there was no gravity in space. Gravity is what keeps our planet orbiting the Sun, and what keeps the Moon rotating in the Earth's orbit, rather than flying off like a slingshot.

ORIGIN: This myth probably has its origins in the (inaccurate) term 'zero gravity', which is widely used to describe conditions in space.

But gravity is everywhere, even in the apparently empty space between galaxies. Astronauts look weightless because they are in continuous freefall toward the Earth, only staying aloft because of their horizontal motion.

Likewise, gravity keeps satellites from flying off into the void. They stay in orbit because of their tremendous horizontal speed, which allows them – while being pulled back to Earth by gravity – to fall 'over the horizon'. The ground's curved withdrawal along the Earth's round surface offsets the satellites' fall toward the ground. It is speed, not lack of gravity, that keeps satellites in space. If their speed drops below a certain point, gravity prevails and they fall back to Earth again.

There's just no escaping gravity!

MYTH!

Like the story that all fingerprints are unique, this is another of those assertions that can never be proved. Unless you were to compare every snowflake that has ever fallen – clearly an impossible task – there is no way of being sure that two or more weren't identical.

ORIGIN: This myth probably arose following the publication of pictures of a wide range of snow crystals by Wilson Bentley in 1931.

Bentley became the first person to photograph single snow crystals, by fixing a microscope to a camera. He published over 5,000 of his 'photomicrographs', and claimed he had 'never seen two snowflakes alike'. And so the legend of no two snowflakes being identical began.

Even so, there is no doubt that snowflakes take a huge variety of forms. At each stage in its growth, a snow crystal has several different 'choices' about how to continue its development. There are many crystal structures available, and therefore many different paths each crystal may take. So a vast number of different shapes could arise. Snow researcher Kenneth Librecht from the California Institute of Technology claims that it's statistically unlikely that two snowflakes will ever be exactly the same, though we could never actually check them all to make sure.

MYTH!

Anyone who has ever looked for constellations such as Orion or Cassiopeia in the night sky will quickly confirm that this is a myth.

Constellations seem to travel in the sky from east to west every night, but they're really not moving. The Earth is moving, rotating on its axis. Constellations also seem to change with the seasons. Again, they're really not changing. They just look that way because the Earth is revolving around the Sun.

ORIGIN: People who make this claim may be getting confused with the fact that the stars always appear in the same place relative to one another. So the Big Dipper always looks the same, but over a period of a year it appears in different places across the night sky. Of course, this is what makes the constellations easily recognizable.

Another thing that sometimes confuses people is that while the stars and constellations always appear in the same place relative to one another, the planets – such as Venus and Jupiter – do not. This is because they are much closer to the Earth than the stars, and like Earth they also orbit the Sun. So you can – for example – always find Sirius by following the line of the three stars in Orion's belt, but there is no easy trick for finding any of the planets.

MYTH!

This is a long-standing myth, but there is no truth in it.

Lightning tends to strike the tallest object around, so tall buildings, bridges, etc. get many strikes. Towers or skyscrapers that reach or exceed 1,000 ft/305 m are virtually guaranteed to take at least one direct hit during any thunderstorm that passes overhead.

ORIGIN: When people quote this saying, they are probably thinking of flat, open country. If a storm passes over such terrain, lightning is just as likely to strike in one place as another, so the chances of two strikes occurring on exactly the same bit of ground are small.

However, even in such conditions it could happen. A strike to any location does nothing to change the electrical activity in the storm above, which will produce another strike as soon as it 'recharges'. And a previously hit location is then just as likely to be struck as any other spot.

But it is really television towers and skyscrapers that blow the 'lightning never strikes twice' myth out of the water. The Sears Tower in Chicago, for example, is struck by lightning 40 to 90 times a year. So if anyone in future tells you 'lightning never strikes the same place twice', just say 'yes it does' and quote this example to them!

MYTH!

This is a common misconception. If it were true, how could steel ships float?

Whether an object will sink or float depends on its density, which is defined as the amount of mass it contains per unit of volume. An object will sink if it weighs more than the water it pushes away, and it will float if it weighs less than the water it pushes away. This was first discovered by the Greek scientist Archimedes.

Anything that floats will still be partly under water. As an object sinks (even by a little) it pushes away water until the amount of water displaced weighs the same as the object that is floating. If an object is too dense to float, this means it cannot push away enough water to equal the amount it weighs. If that happens, the object will sink.

ORIGIN: To many people it seems 'obvious' that whether an object will float or sink depends on its weight. Indeed, when building ships from metal rather than wood was first proposed, many mocked the idea, convinced that such vessels would never float.

In fact, though, because of their shape, which includes plenty of air, ships are less dense than the water they float on. But, of course, if the metal sides of a ship are breached and water gets in, this increases the vessel's overall density, and ultimately – if the whole hull becomes flooded – it will indeed sink.

MYTH!

Even if you dropped a penny from the top of the Empire State Building (not that you'd be allowed to), it would be highly unlikely to cause anyone below any damage. Pennies are simply too small and light, and not aerodynamic in shape.

ORIGIN: When people make this claim, they are ignoring air resistance, which has a considerable slowing-down effect on small objects as they fall. That applies especially to pennies, as they are not aerodynamic and typically flutter to the ground.

A falling penny reaches its highest speed (what scientists call its 'terminal velocity') after about 50 ft/15 m. After that, in a normal atmosphere, the penny coasts at the same speed until it hits the ground. A penny falling from a tall building might sting a bit if it caught you at the wrong angle, but it certainly wouldn't kill you.

Some things would be dangerous to drop from the top of a tall building however. An example would be a ballpoint pen, which due to its streamlined shape could reach up to 200 miles per hour. At such speed it definitely could cause serious damage to a pedestrian (though probably not kill them). The message is clear therefore – small coins might not be too dangerous, but NEVER empty your handbag out at the top of a tall building!

MYTH!

The theory behind this is that the storm causes the air pressure outside to drop so quickly that if you don't keep a window open to allow the pressure to equalize, your windows might explode outward.

In practice, however, leaving windows open actually makes it more likely your house will suffer severe damage.

ORIGIN: Keeping some windows slightly open was at one time recommended as a defense against tornadoes, but the advice has since been discredited.

In the wake of certain tornadoes, it would sometimes look as though a few houses had exploded. From this evidence, scientists theorized that air pressure outside must have been far lower than it was inside, with the difference causing the blowout. It was therefore suggested that people leave their windows open a little to equalize pressure.

Further research, however, showed that those blasted-apart houses were the result of wind blowing into open windows – so the advice, rather than preventing destruction, could actually have caused it. Gusts entering pushed up the roofs at the same time the wind was blowing over them. This made the roofs act like airplane wings and generate lifting force. Once roofs lift off, the walls of houses can fall outward, making it look as if they exploded.

By far the best policy is to keep all your windows closed (and shuttered) during a storm, therefore.

54 All metals are attracted to a magnet

MYTH!

Children in particular often think that all metals are attracted to magnets. However, it is only iron, steel (though not all steels), cobalt and nickel that are attracted to magnets.

ORIGIN: Comic books and cartoons often give the impression that a powerful magnet will attract any metal. It can be a good source of humor in animated films.

This fact is used in recycling plants to separate aluminum cans – which are not magnetic – from 'tins' (actually mostly iron), which are.

55 Eating carrots improves your eyesight

MYTH!

This is only true if you have poor eyesight caused by a deficiency of Vitamin A. Most people eating a nutritious, balanced diet today will not be deficient in this vitamin, so they will not gain any benefit to their sight from eating carrots.

ORIGIN: Carrots contain a substance called beta-carotene, which is turned by the body into Vitamin A. Lack of Vitamin A can cause poor vision, including night vision. In such cases, eating more carrots will provide extra Vitamin A and help your vision improve.

Most people do get enough Vitamin A in their diet, although millions of people in the developing world are believed to suffer from Vitamin A deficiency.

MYTH!

Admittedly, most brain cell growth takes place during our early years, but we continue to grow new brain cells until well into old age.

Severe mental decline is usually caused by disease. By contrast, most age-related losses in memory and cognitive skills simply result from inactivity and a lack of mental exercise and stimulation. In other words, use it or lose it!

ORIGIN: Until quite recently it was widely believed that we didn't grow new brain cells but recent scientific studies have disproved that. In fact America scientists have identified chemicals which stimulate new growth, vital for treating mental disabilities.

However, the main brain growth after childhood and adolescence comes in the dendrites – tiny nerve fibers that connect our brain cells with one another. They are closely associated with memory and learning. Evidence suggests that when we use our brains, more dendrites grow, connecting our brain cells with one another in complex patterns. Throughout life, your brain cells reorganize themselves in response to new experiences. This interaction between your mind and your body is what stimulates brain cells to grow and connect with one another. Until your early teens, various windows of opportunity open when you can most easily learn language and writing, music and mathematics, as well as the co-ordinated movements used in sports and dance. But whatever your age, you can – and should – continue to build your brain and expand your mind.

MYTH!

The story goes that if you accidentally shake a soda can, you should lightly tap it several times before opening it. This is supposed to calm the pressure overload that causes the soda to explode out when the seal is broken.

This is an urban myth, however. The only thing tapping the can achieves is using up a few seconds. During this time some of the gas released by shaking the can is reabsorbed by the liquid, meaning less soda shoots out when the can is opened.

ORIGIN: This is another of those myths that has been around so long it's impossible to know where it originated. It may contain a grain of truth, as during the time you spend tapping the can, some gas will be reabsorbed by the soda.

It's easy enough to show this is a myth, however (if you don't mind getting wet!). Take two soda cans and shake both equally. Tap one a few times and leave the other alone. Then open both at the same time. There will be no difference between the amounts of soda that shoot out.

If you want to reduce the amount lost when a shaken soda can is opened, the best advice is to put it in the fridge for a few minutes. In cool conditions, liquids such as soda can absorb more gas, so the pressure in the can will be reduced.

MYTH!

This 'amazing statistic' regularly appears on trivia lists, yet it is definitely untrue.

The total world population today is approaching seven billion. This is roughly the same number of people who have died since the age of the pyramids (i.e. about 5,000 years ago).

And yet, human history goes back a lot longer than that. Modern human beings are believed to have emerged around 40,000 to 45,000 years ago. Estimates about the number of dead in human history vary widely, from about 12 billion to 110 billion. However, most experts reckon the number of dead at approximately 60 billion, which means that there are several dead ancestors for each one of us.

ORIGIN: It is, of course, true that in the last 100 years or so, the world's population has exploded. In 1800 it was under a billion, and since then it has grown almost seven-fold. So it is probably true that there are more people alive today than have died in the last 5,000 years, which is a pretty staggering statistic in itself. But even if this trend continues, it's unlikely that the number of those alive will ever exceed the number who have died.

MYTH!

Poppy seeds do contain opiates (morphine and codeine), which can be detected in a person's urine after they have eaten them.

It's only a very low concentration, however. Eating a single poppy seed bagel would be highly unlikely to introduce enough opiates into your bloodstream to make you test positive at current testing thresholds.

ORIGIN: Drug tests can detect any level of opiates in your bloodstream even after eating a small amount of poppy seeds. In the past, this has indeed sometimes led to unjustified accusations of drug-taking.

For example, in 1997 a Florida woman was awarded $859,000 in damages against Bankers Insurance Group after it withdrew a job offer due to poppy-seed-influenced drug-test results. And in 1999, a New Jersey prison guard was fired from his job after giving a positive result after eating a poppy seed bagel. He was reinstated when the true facts came to light.

Cases such as these caused the standard cut-off level for opiate urine tests to be raised from the previous 300 ng/ml (nanograms per milliliter) to 2,000 ng/ml, a level much less likely to produce 'false positives'. The US military has gone even further, increasing the threshold to 3,000 ng/ml.

Eating a single poppy seed bagel will typically produce a maximum blood opiate level of 250 ng/ml – so, at current thresholds, it's unlikely that eating even an entire poppy seed loaf would produce a positive test result.

MYTH!

There is no evidence for this proposition, and in fact plenty against it.

One example comes from studies of people with brain damage. If 90 per cent of the brain is normally unused, damage to these areas should not impair performance. Instead, there is almost no area of the brain that can be damaged without loss of abilities. Even small areas of damage can have major effects.

ORIGIN: This story may have its origins in misunderstandings of research in the late 1800s or early 1900s, when scientists announced that they had only been able to map the function of 10 per cent of the brain. Albert Einstein is also reported as quipping that people typically only use 10 per cent of their brains.

The myth has been perpetuated in advertising and by various self-styled gurus. Often, the suggestion is made that by following some secret (and probably expensive) procedure, a person may harness this unused potential and boost their brainpower many times over.

In fact, while many aspects of intelligence may be increased with training, the idea that large parts of the brain remain unused is without foundation. Although many mysteries remain regarding how our brains work, every area of the brain now has a known function.

So no, people don't use only 10 per cent of their brains, though when you watch the news on TV, you might think so at times!

MYTH!

A lot of people believe this, but it's not true. It's unlikely the ostrich would have survived as a species if it really responded to danger in this way!

ORIGIN: This myth probably arose as a result of an optical illusion. Ostriches are the largest living birds, but their heads are relatively small. If you see one picking at the ground from a distance, it may really look as if its head is buried in the ground.

In reality ostriches don't bury their heads in the sand – if they did, they wouldn't be able to breathe. But they do dig holes as nests for their eggs. Several times a day, a mother bird will put her head in the hole and turn the eggs. At these times it can certainly look as though the birds are burying their heads in the sand.

In fact, when an ostrich senses danger it normally runs away (and they are good runners, reaching speeds of up to 45 mph/72 kph). If this is not possible, however, it flops to the ground and remains still, with its head and neck flat on the ground in front of it. Because the head and neck are light in color, they blend in with the color of the soil. From a distance it can look as if the ostrich has buried its head in the sand, as only the body is visible.

For all these reasons, it's not surprising that this myth is so widely believed!

MYTH!

This is one of those stories we've all heard and many of us believe to be true. You can argue that there are any number of man-made structures visible from space, or none at all, depending entirely on how far away from Earth you are when viewing it.

From the international space station (400 km/250 miles up), with the naked eye it is difficult to pick out any manmade structure. With binoculars or a strong telescope you can make out things like highways, the Egyptian Pyramids, the Great Wall and even airplane contrails.

In 1965 whislt orbiting Earth, Gemini V astronauts Gordon Cooper and Charles Conrad claimed they were able to spot, among other things, a special checkerboard pattern that had been laid out in Texas and the aircraft carrier that would later pick them up in the Atlantic, along with a destroyer trailing in its wake.

ORIGIN: It's not known exactly where this story originated, although some people believe it was a throwaway remark made at an after-dinner speech during the early years of the space program. Since then, it has been repeated so many times that many people believe it must be true.

A lot depends on how far from the Earth you are, though. Astronaut Alan Bean wrote: 'The only thing you can see from the Moon is a beautiful sphere, mostly white (clouds), some blue (ocean), patches of yellow (deserts), and every once in a while some green vegetation. No manmade object is visible on this scale. In fact, when first leaving Earth's orbit and only a few thousand miles away, no man-made object is visible at that point either.'

63

MYTH!

This is one of those theories that sounds plausible but wouldn't work in practice.

If you're in a falling elevator, both you and the elevator are descending at the same speed. If you jump, you will be moving at the same speed minus your jumping speed. An elevator can fall at up to 32 ft/9.7 m per second, while the highest jump ever recorded by a human being is 8 ft/2.5 m.

If you were in a very tall elevator, you would therefore have to duplicate this eight-foot jump in just a quarter of a second to counteract the fall. The odds against anyone doing this at exactly the right moment are infinitesimal

ORIGIN: This myth may have started in 1945, when Betty Lou Oliver plummeted 75 stories down the Empire State Building in a loose elevator. She claimed she survived because she jumped just before the elevator hit the bottom. In reality, though, it was probably the air pressure in the shaft that slowed her descent just enough to be survivable.

If you are trapped in a falling elevator (unlikely due to all the built-in safety measures) the best advice is to lie on your stomach and cover your head. This spreads the force across your body – and if any debris falls from the top of the elevator, your head and vital organs are less likely to be hit.

MYTH!

Contrary to what happens in certain films, quicksand doesn't suck you down. Rather, anyone who steps into it will sink just as they would in any other liquid. But unless they are carrying a very heavy load (a full backpack, for example) that makes them less buoyant, they will sink only to their chest or shoulders.

ORIGIN: 'Deadly quicksand' often features in movies and dime store novels, as it is a handy source of dramatic tension. The reality is much less scary, though.

As quicksand is very thick, if someone is wearing heavy boots they may encounter a lot of suction and resistance. However, quicksand does not have any magical, magnetic property that pulls you into it!

A person who has stepped into quicksand can usually get out without much difficulty, even after sinking halfway to their knees. The difficulty in getting out of quicksand is not because it grabs you and holds you, but because you end up floating in a semi-liquid sludge, with no solid ground to pull yourself out.

If you are caught in quicksand, drop anything you are carrying and, if possible, remove your shoes. Because your body is less dense than quicksand, you can't fully sink unless you panic and struggle too much. Take your time, breathe deeply, and float on your back if you feel your muscles getting tired. Call for help if anyone is nearby, and make your way back to more solid ground.

65 Paper grocery bags are better for the environment than plastic ones

MYTH!

The main criticisms of plastic bags are that they use up natural resources, are toxic in marine environments and take a long time to decompose. This may be true, but the manufacture of paper bags uses lots of trees, which is also bad for the environment.

ORIGIN: Many people believe paper bags are better than plastic because they biodegrade faster. What is better is the introduction of bags made using renewable resources such as corn, though. These bags degrade in months instead of centuries. And because they are made from agricultural products, they aren't as harmful to the environment.

66 A human soprano voice can shatter a wine glass

MYTH!

There is no documented proof of a soprano ever doing this. In 2005, though, the Discovery Channel TV show MythBusters recruited rock singer Jamie Vendera (not a soprano) to make an attempt. He tried twelve wine glasses, and eventually did get one to shatter.

ORIGIN: The idea behind this is that every piece of glass has a natural resonant frequency. If a person sings that exact note, in theory the glass will start vibrating at that frequency, and eventually shake itself to bits. In practice, though, the singer would have to hit exactly the right note at high volume, and even then the glass would need to have flaws.

MYTH!

This is another of those urban legends that has been going around for some time. Indeed, so widely circulated has it become that many gas station owners have put up warning messages at the pumps telling people to switch off their phones.

There is, however, no authenticated evidence that using a cellphone near a gas pump has ever directly caused an explosion.

ORIGIN: The earliest rumors connecting cellphones with starting fires have been traced back to a 1999 article in China Post. This alleged that an Indonesian driver was badly burned when 'a spark from the static electricity in the mobile [phone] ignited the petrol vapor', blowing up his car.

Although this story was never confirmed, some cautious petroleum industry executives took it seriously, partly because some cellphone manuals shipped during the 1990s contained warnings against using the products anywhere gasoline vapors might be present. But the danger was, and is, purely theoretical.

A 2001 investigation by the Center for the Study of Wireless Electromagnetic Compatibility at the University of Oklahoma found 'virtually no evidence to suggest that cellphones pose a hazard at gas stations'. Nonetheless, the myth persists to this day, regularly reinforced by hoax emails warning of the dire consequences of using cellphones at gas stations, and asking the recipient to forward the warning to all their friends.

MYTH!

For many years this was widely believed to be true, but it was disproved by Britney Crystal Gallivan (born 1985) of Pomona, California.

In January 2002, while a junior in high school, Gallivan demonstrated that a single piece of toilet paper 4000 feet in length could be folded in half twelve times.

Gallivan calculated that instead of folding in half every other direction, the best way to get twelve folds would be to fold in the same direction, using a very long sheet of paper. Not only did she demonstrate this herself, she also derived an equation that revealed the width (or length) of paper needed to fold a piece of paper of any given thickness any specified number of times.

ORIGIN: Folding a piece of paper in half more than seven times was commonly believed to be impossible. Over the years the problem was discussed by many people, including mathematicians, and 'proven' to be impossible on many TV programs.

It's no surprise, then, that most people believed this myth. And the fact that it was disproved by a high-school student who did it to gain an extra credit for her mathematics class is all the more amazing. Britney Gallivan and her feat went on to achieve further fame when they were mentioned in the Season 1 episode 'Identity Crisis' (2005) of the television crime drama NUMB3RS!

MYTH!

An elephant cowering at the sight of a tiny mouse is a staple of the cartoonist, but there is no truth in the legend.

Elephants are among the most fearless of animals, even though they share their natural habitats with lions, rhinos, and tigers (though that same fearlessness, unfortunately, can also make them easy prey for poachers).

Elephants are more likely to encounter mice in zoos and circuses (where the amount of grain and hay tend to attract the creatures) than in the wild – but, either way, there is nothing about mice that they find particularly scary.

ORIGIN: If there is any basis for this myth, it comes from elephants being anxious about nearby sounds or movements they can't identify, such as might be caused by mice foraging around for food. Elephants may be afraid of very little, but unusual sounds and small, fast objects that are difficult to follow can add up to something unfamiliar, and that could signal 'danger' to them. However, such a reaction could just as easily be triggered by something other than mice, such as a small dog.

In fact, given the elephant's large size and notoriously poor eyesight, any mouse getting too close to one would have a lot more to worry about than the elephant does!

MYTH!

The common cold is caused by a virus which is transmitted from one person to another. Being out in freezing weather has no effect on this.

ORIGIN: From ancient times people noticed that colds and flu are more common in cold weather. The very name 'cold' implies that the disease is somehow caused by the climate.

It's not the case, though. During cold weather people are in closer contact with one another, so viruses are more likely to be passed on. In addition, research has shown that cold viruses are more easily transmitted in dry air, as often occurs in houses and offices in winter when the heating is switched on.

In tropical areas, where it doesn't get cold, the peak time for colds and flu is during the rainy season. But again, these illnesses are not caused by the rain. They are just more prevalent because people come into closer contact with one another than they do in the dry season.

To avoid catching colds, the most important thing is to protect yourself against germs when you are around other people. Viruses are passed on by contact between people or things they have touched, so be sure to wash your hands often. Going out in the cold may actually be a healthy thing to do, if it gets you away from other people and their viruses!

MYTH!

This is a long-standing belief in many cultures, but there is no scientific evidence to show any link between the phases of the moon and insanity.

ORIGIN: This is one of the most enduring myths in human history, deeply embedded in folklore and popular culture, from the myth of the werewolf to Creedence Clearwater Revival's massive 1969 hit, 'Bad Moon Rising'. The word 'lunacy' has its roots in the Latin word for moon.

Studies have found that police officers and hospital workers are among the strongest believers in the theory that more crime and trauma occur on nights when the moon is full. One 1995 University of New Orleans study found that as many as 81 per cent of mental health professionals believed the myth.

Although there is no evidence for any direct link between the full moon and insanity, it's possible there may be an indirect one. Because such nights are brighter, more people may be out and about till late, making incidents of all kinds more likely. In addition, the greater brightness may cause sleep deprivation, which can lead to manic episodes in people who are already disposed to this.

But there is nothing particular about a full moon that can cause you to go mad.

MYTH!

Although you may have seen the James Bond film Goldfinger where this happens to actress Shirley Eaton, there is no truth in it.

We breathe through our nose and mouth, not through our skin. A person painted all over in gold paint might eventually die of overheating because they are unable to perspire, but they wouldn't suffocate.

ORIGIN: At the time Goldfinger was made (1964), it was still widely believed that we breathe through our skin, and that closing off all the pores in one's body with paint would therefore result in death by asphyxiation. Indeed, as a precaution during the filming, a square was left unpainted on the actress's abdomen to allow her skin to 'breathe'.

We now know this to be mistaken. As long as a person can breathe through their mouth and/or nose, they won't die of asphyxiation, no matter how much of their body is covered with paint or anything else.

That isn't to say that painting yourself all over doesn't carry some risks. It could eventually cause death by overheating. And toxic substances in the paint could also poison you if the paint was kept on too long.

On the whole, it's probably best to keep that gold paint for the garden railings!

MYTH!

If you include mountains that are partly under water, there are several taller than Everest.

The distinction of being the world's tallest mountain actually goes to Mauna Kea in Hawaii. Mauna Kea is an island, and if the distance from the bottom of the nearby ocean floor to the peak of the island is measured, then Mauna Kea is taller than Mount Everest. Mauna Kea is over 32,808 ft/10,000 m tall, compared to 29,029 ft/8,848 m for Mount Everest.

ORIGIN: Mount Everest is indeed the highest mountain above sea level. It beats the next highest, K2, by 777 ft/237 m. But, it's definitely not the tallest.

In fact, depending on how you define height, there is another mountain that can claim the title of the world's highest mountain: Mount Chimborazo in Ecuador. This has an altitude of 20,702 ft/6,310 m, which is less than both Mount Everest and Mauna Kea. However, Chimborazo has the distinction of being the highest mountain above Earth's center.

The reason for this is that the Earth is not a perfect sphere – it bulges around the equator. Chimborazo is just one degree south of the equator, and at that location it is about 1.25 m/2 km farther from Earth's center than Mount Everest.

If you define 'highest' as distance above sea level, Mount Everest is still the champion. But if you want to stand on the place on Earth that is closest to the moon, that would be Mount Chimborazo!

MYTH!

Many people believe drinking alcohol kills brain cells – and even medical students are taught this. It's not true, though. Pure alcohol does indeed kill cells of all types, but there's no evidence that drinking alcohol does. Legal intoxication is reached when the concentration of alcohol in the bloodstream reaches a mere 0.1 per cent. That's a big difference from the almost 100 per cent solutions used for sterilizing. One thing drinking alcohol definitely doesn't do is wipe out brain cells like disinfectant.

ORIGIN: Obviously, alcohol does have an effect on the brain. Anyone who drinks enough to get drunk is likely to end up with slurred speech and impaired judgment, among other side-effects. They are also likely to suffer from headaches, nausea and other unpleasant symptoms afterwards.

Even in alcoholics, however, alcohol use doesn't actually result in the death of brain cells. A 1993 study by Grethe Jensen and colleagues proved this by carefully counting the brain cells in matched samples of alcoholics and nonalcoholics who had died of causes unrelated to drinking. When the two groups were compared, no significant differences in the overall number of brain cells were found.

The latest research, however, has found that heavy drinking can damage the ends of brain cells, called dendrites. This results in problems conveying messages. The cell itself isn't damaged, but the way it communicates with others is altered. The good news is that this damage is mostly reversible if you stop drinking, though.

MYTH!

Alcohol will not warm you up in cold weather. In fact, it is likely to chill you, although it causes a chain reaction to give you illusory warmth while your body is actually being cooled. This makes the effect of drinking alcohol outdoors twice as dangerous.

ORIGIN: When you are cold, your body uses a variety of defenses to try to warm you up and avoid losing any more heat. Shivering, for example, is a way of warming up your body through physical action.

Normally, in cold weather, our body diverts blood away from the surface to the inside. This reduces heat loss through the skin, and ensures that our vital organs are kept warm and well supplied with oxygen.

Alcohol, however, interferes with this response. It causes the capillaries – small blood vessels near the surface of the skin – to dilate. More blood comes to the body's surface, and the person may look flushed. If you are out in cold weather this can be dangerous, as it means you will be losing more heat through your skin.

Drinking alcohol can also impair your judgment, and your sensitivity to heat and cold. For all these reasons, if you're chilled it's best to go inside and warm up by a roaring fire – and only then, perhaps, drink a glass of something cheering.

76 Hypnotists can influence unwilling patients

MYTH!

ORIGIN: This myth has been popularized by stage and TV hypnotists, who appear to be able to make people do embarrassing things under hypnosis. This is easily explained, though. Many people enjoy getting the chance to show off and have fun, and the hypnotist is skilled at judging who would like to take part. People who don't want to do it don't get called, and people who are especially unwilling don't attend in the first place.

Many experiments have proved that people can't be forced to do anything that is truly against their will, either during a hypnotic session or afterwards. Any such suggestion is always rejected.

77 Yodeling can set off an avalanche

MYTH!

ORIGIN: Like deadly quicksand, this is a popular plot device in novels and movies. And there is even less truth in it than the quicksand myth.

Avalanches are a serious matter, as every year around 150 people worldwide are killed by them. They are not caused by noise, however. Avalanches actually occur when a weak layer in the snow can no longer support the weight of a stronger layer above it and collapses, causing a rapid flow of snow down the slope. This can be caused by various things, including heavy rain or snow, sudden warming, or human activity such as skiers or snowmobiles. There are no known cases of yodeling causing one, though!

MYTH!

Sloths are small South American mammals that move very slowly, when they move at all. Scientists say their sluggishness is caused by their low metabolic rate and low body temperature (91°F/33°C). This allows them to eat very slowly (and to only need a small amount of food), because they don't expend much energy.

Sloths were also once believed to sleep for more than 16 hours a day, but this may be due to their having being studied in captivity. A 2008 research project led by Dr. Niels Rattenborg and published in the journal Biology Letters studied sloths in the wild, and found that such animals slept for under 10 hours. The difference is likely to be because captive sloths do not have to stay awake to hunt for food.

ORIGIN: Sloths may have acquired their reputation for laziness because of their slow-moving lifestyles. They are far from being the doziest animals, though.

Dogs typically sleep for 10 hours a day, cats for 12, and pythons an impressive 18 hours. The prize for the laziest animal should probably go to the Brown Bat, however, which sleeps for almost 20 hours out of every 24. That's some slumber party!

MYTH!

Lots of parents believe this, but scientific studies have shown it to be a myth. There is no direct evidence linking sugar consumption with hyperactivity.

ORIGIN: This story has its roots in an article published in 1977 in the trade journal Food and Cosmetics Toxicology. This described a three-year study of how sugar was processed by juvenile ADHD (Attention Deficit Hyperactivity Disorder) patients. It found that a majority of these children had abnormal results from a glucose tolerance test.

The study did not explain the connection (and neither has any subsequent study), but at the time many parents interpreted it to mean that too much sugar was a cause of hyperactivity.

Since then, though, many studies have failed to show any connection. In particular, research has suggested that parents often interpret hyperactivity as a reaction to something their child has eaten. Often, though, sweet things are consumed at parties and other social occasions, where excitement is running high anyway. Any hyperactivity may therefore be caused by social rather than food-related factors.

On the other hand, sugary foods are often also high in additives, and there is some evidence that these may indeed cause hyperactivity in some children. More research is needed to confirm this – but for now it seems that parents wanting a quieter life might still be advised to cut back on the cakes and candy!

MYTH!

Poinsettias are beautiful plants with an unjustified toxic reputation. Every year at Christmas dire warnings are circulated about the need to prevent children and pets from eating the leaves, and the possibly lethal consequences of doing so.

The truth is that poinsettias are NOT poisonous. They are not actually edible, and if eaten in quantity can cause stomach upsets and possible vomiting. You would probably have to devour several plants to produce this effect, however (unlikely, due to their bitter, unpalatable flavor). In the case of a child who eats a single leaf, no ill effects would be expected.

ORIGIN: This myth is believed to have originated in 1919, when the two-year-old child of an army officer stationed in Hawaii died of poisoning, and the cause was incorrectly assumed to be eating a poinsettia leaf. There are actually no proven cases of anyone, adult or child, dying from eating a poinsettia.

It's possible that one reason for the tenacity of this myth is that poinsettias belong to the genus Euphorbia, which includes many species that are highly toxic. Poinsettias are not among them, though.

Because of the belief that the plants are toxic, every year there are numerous visits to hospitals by parents concerned that their children may have eaten poinsettias. A study in 2000 by the Children's Hospital of Pittsburgh and Carnegie Mellon University, however, found that out of nearly 23,000 poinsettia exposures reported nationwide, not one example of a toxic reaction was found.

MYTH!

We've all heard about animals, often household pets, who apparently predicted some natural disaster hours or days before it happened. Despite extensive studies, however, no evidence has been found that animals possess a sixth sense that can predict such occurrences.

ORIGIN: There is most likely to be a natural explanation for this myth, and even perhaps an element of truth in it. Animals typically have more finely-tuned senses than humans, which they need for hunting prey and avoiding predators. These senses can also give them an early warning of impending disasters. In the case of earthquakes, some scientists believe animals sense the first vibrations before human beings notice them. Another theory is that they detect changes in the air or gases released by the earth when such upheavals occur. It might be correct then to say that animals may sense natural disasters, but not predict them.

There is no shortage of stories about animals apparently sensing natural disasters. Hours before the December 2004 tsunami, for example, many wild animals in Sri Lanka's Yala National Park moved to higher ground, thus avoiding mass deaths when the tsunami struck.

The United States Geological Survey has officially announced that 'changes in animal behavior cannot be used to predict earthquakes'. As well as referring to animals' more finely tuned senses, they pointed out that animals change their behavior for many reasons. Given that an earthquake can affect millions of people, it is likely that a few pets will, by chance, be acting strangely just before a quake. Rather than proving their predictive powers, however, this might simply indicate that they wanted their supper!

MYTH!

Airplane toilets do create suction when flushed in order to remove the contents of the bowl. There is no evidence that this has ever led to anybody getting stuck on one however.

One reason for this is that it is almost impossible to get a perfect seal on a modern airplane toilet. Even if it was possible, a properly working toilet provides suction for only a few seconds. And even then, the suction is so slight that it's not beyond most people's ability to overcome.

ORIGIN: This 'urban myth' came from a widely circulated 2002 Reuters news story. This claimed that a female passenger had filed a complaint about the toilet on a Scandinavian Airlines flight. In fact, this 'true story' turned out to come from a training exercise for airline staff. There was no actual passenger stuck on a toilet seat.

Even so, the suction from an airplane toilet could be uncomfortable if you're sitting on it, so for that reason it's best to stand up before flushing. In fact, in the next generation of passenger planes such as Boeing's Dreamliner 787, flushing while standing will be your only option. Lavatories on these planes have touchless flush mechanisms that automatically put the lid down before flushing the toilet.

MYTH!

Although margarine is often presented as a healthier alternative to butter for this reason, it's not the case. Butter and margarine contain different types of fat, but in similar amounts. Unfortunately, this means both may be unhealthy for different reasons.

The fat in butter is mainly saturated fat. Eating saturated fats in quantity has been known for some time to cause hardening of the arteries, potentially leading to heart attacks or strokes.

Margarine is lower in saturated fat than butter, but it is more likely to contain hydrogenated fats. There is growing evidence that hydrogenated fats, also called trans-fats, may be even more harmful than saturated fats. Not only do they raise cholesterol levels, they can block the important utilization of essential fatty acids in the body. Trans-fats have been linked with many conditions and diseases, including cancer, Alzheimer's disease, obesity, diabetes, and so on.

ORIGIN: The confusion may have come about through advertisements claiming that margarine was superior to butter because of its lower saturated fat content. This health claim appeared to have some basis for many years, as it's only quite recently that the dangers of trans-fats have become known.

If you want to eat healthily, it's best to keep your consumption of both butter and margarine to a minimum. A little butter is fine now and then as a luxury, but don't use any margarine or spread that doesn't state on the tub that it's free or almost free of trans-fats.

MYTH!

Drinking ice-water does burn a few more calories compared with drinking warm water. That's because, when you drink the ice-water, your body will expend a few calories bringing it to body temperature. In weight-loss terms the benefits are negligible, though.

According to Dr. Roger Clemens, Associate Director of Regulatory Science of the University of Southern California School of Pharmacy, drinking one eight-ounce glass of ice-water would burn up about eight calories. That's about the number of calories you get in a single cashew nut.

Based on these figures, it would take around 435 eight-ounce glasses of ice-water to lose a pound. And consuming such large quantities of cold water could have serious health effects, such as a lowering of your body temperature, digestive problems, and even anemia. Drinking a lot of water in a short time can also lead to water intoxication, a serious condition that is sometimes fatal.

ORIGIN: This is obviously an attractive idea and it does have a small measure of truth to it. Drinking ice-water alone, however, is unlikely to produce any significant weight loss, unless you drink so much that you put other aspects of your health at risk.

Ten minutes' cycling will burn off 100 calories – for which benefit you'd have to drink over twelve eight-ounce glasses of ice-water – and give you healthy exercise and fresh air as well. Better get the bike out instead!

MYTH!

This is certainly a myth, but it would be correct to say that cats *usually* land on their feet. But, as any cat owner will tell you, it doesn't happen every time.

ORIGIN: This is another of those myths that has such a measure of truth to it that it is easy to see how it originated.

Cats, even very young kittens, have an amazing sense of balance. When they are falling, the fluid in their inner ear shifts and the cat rotates its head until it equalizes and the fluid is level. The body automatically shifts to follow the head, and the cat lands on its feet.

It also helps that cats are extremely agile, and their supple muscles and spine respond instantly. A cat has 30 vertebrae. That is five more than humans, which accounts in part for their amazing agility.

Although cats can survive a long fall (the unofficial record is 18 stories), if you're a cat owner living in an upstairs apartment it's still very important to watch for open windows, as cats can still incur severe injuries when landing on their feet, especially on a hard surface.

Strangely enough, though, some of the most serious injuries to cats occur in falls from 10 to 12 feet. In falls of this distance there often simply isn't enough time for even an agile cat to complete the full switch to 'feet-side down'.

MYTH!

This is a popular myth in the playground, and even some adults believe it. It's not true, though.

Closing your eyes when you sneeze is a powerful reflex. A few people's eyes don't shut when they sneeze, but most people's do.

Your eyes won't pop out if you deliberately hold them open during a sneeze, though. If it really was the case that our eyes were only held in by our eyelids, one good slap on the back would send them flying!

Some people believe the eyes close as a defense mechanism, to keep all the germs and particles expelled when you sneeze out of the eye. But that's unlikely to be the case, as the force of a sneeze sends all these unpleasant substances away from the face, not toward it.

ORIGIN: Because closing your eyes when you sneeze is such a powerful reflex, many people assume there must be a good reason for it. Scientists have been unable to discover one, however. It appears to be just an involuntary reaction with no real purpose.

The eyes may close during a sneeze in the same way your leg kicks out when your knee is tapped. The body is hard-wired to produce this action, but there's no obvious reason for it. It's a reflex that may have performed some useful function way back in human history, but serves no purpose now.

MYTH!

This 'fact' is sometimes quoted by vegetarians as the reason they don't eat meat. It's not true, though. Meat generally leaves the stomach in 2–3 hours and is fully digested in 4–6 hours. Our digestive system is well designed to digest meat, in order to use its wide range of nutrients.

ORIGIN: It's true that meat is more satisfying than many other foods, particularly over a period of time. This means we feel full for longer.

Why this happens is not yet fully understood, although scientists believe it's due to meat's effect on the messengers in our brain. But this definitely doesn't mean it's not being digested.

88 Your hair will start to clean itself if you leave it unwashed for long enough

MYTH!

Hair doesn't magically clean itself. If you leave it unwashed, it will just get dirtier. The result is likely to be an irritated, itchy scalp and greasy, bad-smelling hair.

ORIGIN: This is a rumor many of us heard at school. There are also tales of people who haven't washed their hair for months and it's never looked better.

In fact, regularly washing using a good shampoo suited to your hair type really is the best way to keep your hair healthy and attractive.

MYTH!

Probably one of the most widely-held myths concerning black holes is that they are black.

According to Einstein's theories of relativity, the gravitational forces associated with black holes are so strong that light cannot escape or be emitted from them. Therefore they are invisible.

ORIGIN: We observe black holes indirectly by their effects on material around them. When viewed from Earth, some black holes do indeed appear as areas of total darkness in space, others appear as yellow, pink or blue depending on where they are. However, calling them black is rather like calling a light bulb that is turned off black because it is not emitting any light.

A black hole is an area of extremely dense matter resulting from the collapse of a star. It has a very high gravitational field, which – again, according to Einstein – distorts time and space around it. Even though nothing, including light, can escape from them, the presence of black holes can be deduced by scientists from the way their powerful gravitational fields affect the stars and other objects surrounding them.

Some scientists believe that with certain types of black hole, it might be possible for something, e.g. a spaceship to enter one and, rather than being absorbed, come out somewhere else in the universe. This is the 'wormhole' so beloved of science-fiction writers. If this proves right, one day human beings really could go 'to infinity and beyond!'

MYTH!

This one is quite plausible, and in fact is only partly a myth. After all, we've all been in situations where one person in a group yawns, then someone else follows suit.

There is no evidence that yawning is contagious in the way that the common cold and flu virus are. But researchers have found that around half of all people are susceptible to 'group' yawning. Suprisingly, the other half aren't affected by it at all.

ORIGIN: We've all seen it happen, but we tend to assume it affects everyone.

One theory is that, far from being a sign that we're ready to sleep, the purpose of yawning is to cool our brain so it operates more efficiently and keeps us awake. If we see someone yawning, therefore, we take it as a sign that we need to be more alert, so we yawn as a way of waking ourselves up.

Scientists have also speculated that it is actually a method of communication within groups.

Another recent study found a close link between contagious yawning and empathy. In other words, people who were more prone to contagious yawning were better at judging other people's feelings and emotions. According to this research, contagious yawning may be a way we communicate our understanding of the people around us and strengthen our emotional bonds with them.

MYTH!

A planet is a celestial body that revolves around a star. The Sun is the star around which the Earth and the other planets of our solar system revolve.

Likewise, the Moon is not a planet, as it does not revolve around a star but the Earth. Many of the other planets in our solar system have moons as well. Jupiter, for example, has at least 63!

ORIGIN: The name 'planet' comes from a Greek word meaning 'wanderer'. They were given this name by the ancient astronomers, who noticed how they moved around the sky in relation to the other stars.

In ancient times it was almost universally believed that the Earth was at the center of the universe and all the stars and planets circled it. The reasons for this were that stars and planets appeared to revolve around the Earth each day, and the apparently commonsense view that the Earth was solid and stable, and that it was not moving but stationary.

It was not until the 16th century that Copernicus and Galileo demonstrated that this was incorrect, and that the Earth and other planets in fact revolved around the Sun.

The fact that some people still believe the Sun is a planet may be due to seeing diagrams and models which show the Sun alongside the planets for comparative purposes. However, the Sun is a star, and like many other stars has planets (such as the Earth) revolving around it.

MYTH!

The story goes that in 1966 Walt Disney, knowing he didn't have long to live, made arrangements for his body to be cryogenically frozen. Since the procedure was only proposed in 1962 and it is accepted that the first person successfully cryonically frozen was in 1967 then it is unlikely that Uncle Walt is in a deep freeze in a secret location.

Rumor has it his body is stored in a chamber somewhere – directly under Disneyland's 'Pirates of the Caribbean' attraction is the most commonly mentioned site – waiting for the day when science is advanced enough to cure his cancer and bring him back to life.

ORIGIN: It's quite possible that Disney might have heard of cryonics, as numerous articles were published about it in the early 1960s. And the first actual cryogenic suspension took place just a month after Disney's death. Stories of his alleged fascination with extending his life with this method did not appear till decades after his death and current scientific methods show little likelihood of restoring human life.

What's more, all the evidence points to the fact that Walt Disney was cremated after his death in 1966. His other family members confirmed that this was his wish, and his death certificate shows he was cremated two days after his death. In addition, a marked burial plot can be found at the Forest Lawn Memorial Park in Glendale, and court papers indicate that the Disney estate paid $40,000 to Forest Lawn for interment property. So while this makes a nice 'conspiracy' story, the evidence against is pretty conclusive.

MYTH!

Hot liquids such as chicken soup can soothe a sore throat and provide fluids to combat dehydration. But chicken soup has no other proven qualities that can help fight a cold.

Colds are basically self-limiting illnesses. There is no 'cure' for one. You just have to wait a few days for your body to get over it on its own.

ORIGIN: Chicken soup is a well-known folk medicine in many cultures. It has been referred to as 'Jewish penicillin', because traditionally Jewish mothers gave it to their children when they were ill. And in China also, hot chicken soup is traditionally given to anyone suffering from a cold to help speed their recovery.

Chicken soup may have acquired this reputation because it is a classic comfort food – tasty and warming, yet also easy to digest.

To confuse matters, some doctors do claim chicken soup may offer genuine benefits for cold sufferers. It has been suggested that it may temporarily speed up the movement of mucus, possibly helping to relieve congestion and cutting the time viruses are in contact with the nose lining. Much more research would be needed to confirm this though. And this is unlikely to happen, because – even if it was proved to be a good treatment for colds – nobody could ever patent chicken soup!

MYTH!

Firstly, whether you run or walk through rain, you will still be struck by the same amount of water so long as the walker and the runner are in the rain for the same amount of time. In other words, you will be hit by the same amount of rain per second.

There is, though, the element of time to consider. If you run, you will reach shelter faster, and therefore be significantly drier. So you actually get less wet if you run, not wetter.

ORIGIN: Many people believe this myth to be true, perhaps because if you run in rain more of it strikes you in the face, which can feel extremely unpleasant. You will also get wetter at the front of your body, where it's most noticeable.

In practice, the decision whether to run or walk often comes down to logistics. If shelter is close by, it makes sense to run to get there before you're soaked through.

If it's further away, however, you might decide to walk instead, as running the entire distance might be impractical, or use up too much energy and possibly be dangerous as well. And if you're already sodden, being out in the rain a bit longer isn't really going to make much difference to you!

MYTH!

SPF stands for Sun Protection Factor. It's a measure of how effective a sunscreen is in blocking the UV-B ultraviolet radiation that causes sunburn.

No sunscreen blocks 100 per cent of ultraviolet rays. A sunscreen with an SPF of 30 protects against 97 per cent, whilst one rated SPF 50 will shut out 98 per cent – just 1 per cent more!

What's more, the higher the SPF, the more harsh chemicals will be in the product, and the more toxins potentially you will be applying to your body.

ORIGIN: It's no surprise people get confused by sunscreen labeling. In particular, to many it seems logical that an SPF 50 sunscreen will provide almost twice the protection of an SPF 30.

SPF labeling can also be misleading as it only refers to protection against the UV-B rays that cause burning. It does not cover the potentially more damaging UV-A rays that can cause premature ageing of the skin and even skin cancer. For that reason, it's important not to choose solely by SPF, but look for a 'broad-spectrum' sunscreen that also blocks UV-A.

Finally, regardless of the SPF or what the label says, sunscreens must be reapplied every 80 minutes or less. Some people mistakenly think a single application of a high-SPF product will protect them all day, when in fact any sunscreen must be reapplied regularly to remain effective.

MYTH!

A base tan is a slow, gradual tan achieved under either natural or artificial sunlight. Many tanning salons recommend getting a base tan as a way of protecting yourself against sunburn before going on beach vacations and tropical cruises.

The theory behind getting a base tan is that your skin gradually builds up color and will therefore be less likely to burn with sudden exposure to the sun. There is, however, little evidence to support this view, and plenty against it. The American Academy of Dermatology and most physicians argue that a base tan does not protect a person from sunburn.

ORIGIN: It's true that having a 'base tan' can reduce the appearance of sunburn. However, it is the UV-A and UV-B radiation in sunlight that causes skin damage, regardless of whether the immediate result is red or brown skin. Any tan is actually a sign that the skin is fighting against damage from sunlight.

Furthermore, many people wrongly believe that getting a base tan reduces the need for sunscreen, and therefore fail to protect themselves adequately.

Whenever you're out in the sun it's still essential to apply a good, broad-spectrum sunblock and reapply it regularly. Not only will this reduce the appearance of sunburn, it will help protect you against skin cancer and premature ageing as well.

MYTH!

The story goes that we swallow these spiders while we're asleep. Thankfully, though, there's no truth in it. Since it is highly unlikely, there have been no studies to date but the legends persist.

ORIGIN: We know exactly where this myth originated. It was invented by PC Professional columnist Lisa Holst, as an example of the ridiculous things people will believe just because they read them on the Internet.

In a 1993 article about lists of 'amazing facts' that were being circulated by email and believed by gullible people, she provided this example, which she obtained from a 1954 book of insect folklore. Ironically, this resulted in it being widely circulated across the Internet, thus proving her point rather well!

The only way this could happen is if you were sleeping with your mouth wide open. If a spider crawled on your face and over your lips, you'd feel it and even in our sleep we have automatic defensive mechanisms. So a spider would have to descend directly into your mouth from above. Your reflexes would probably wake you up immediately if it landed on your sensitive tongue. Furthermore, spiders see humans as giant predators so would not approach a huge, heavy-breathing beast, especially if it was snoring.

98

We experience seasons because of the Earth's changing distance from the Sun

MYTH!

If this was the reason we experienced seasons, it would be the same the world over. In fact, when it's summer in the northern hemisphere, it's winter in the southern hemisphere, and vice versa. The real reason we have seasons is because the Earth tilts by 23.5° with respect to its orbital plane. The reason it's summer in the northern hemisphere is because the North Pole tilts toward the Sun at that time.

ORIGIN: To many people it seems 'obvious' the seasons are caused by Earth's changing distance from the Sun. However, a quick trip to the opposite hemisphere would soon change their mind!

99

Lemon juice dissolves fat

MYTH!

The story goes that sprinkling lemon juice on the fat on meat dissolves it. This is false – lemon juice doesn't dissolve fat. The best way to reduce the fat on meat is to trim it off or choose leaner cuts.

ORIGIN: Nobody knows how this myth started. But lemon juice does have many other useful qualities. For example, the acid in lemon juice can hydrolise the tough fibers in meat, making it more tender. It's high in Vitamin C. And there's no denying that a twist of lemon juice gives fish an extra zing. But squeezing it on your meat definitely won't help you lose weight!

MYTH!

Windows filter out some of the ultraviolet radiation that causes sunburn, but not all of it. What's more, glass is better at blocking the UV-B radiation that causes sunburn than the UV-A radiation which can cause premature skin ageing and skin cancer.

ORIGIN: For the reason above, it's true that you will burn (or tan) more slowly behind glass, but given enough exposure you will still burn.

You may suffer more severe consequences too. In the United States, most skin cancers are on the left side of the face, chest and arms, because people sit on the left while driving, and the sun strikes them on that side through the car windows.

So if you sit for a long time in cars or conservatories on sunny days, you should still wear sun protection.

A note on spelling:
Since this edition is sold worldwide we
have used American English spellings throughout.